The Laidley Worm Of Bamborough

A Northumbrian Tale

THE LAIDLEY WORM OF BAMBOROUGH
is based on a traditional ballad with additional
verses by Joan Henderson.

Published by Newcastle upon Tyne
City Libraries & Arts, 1991

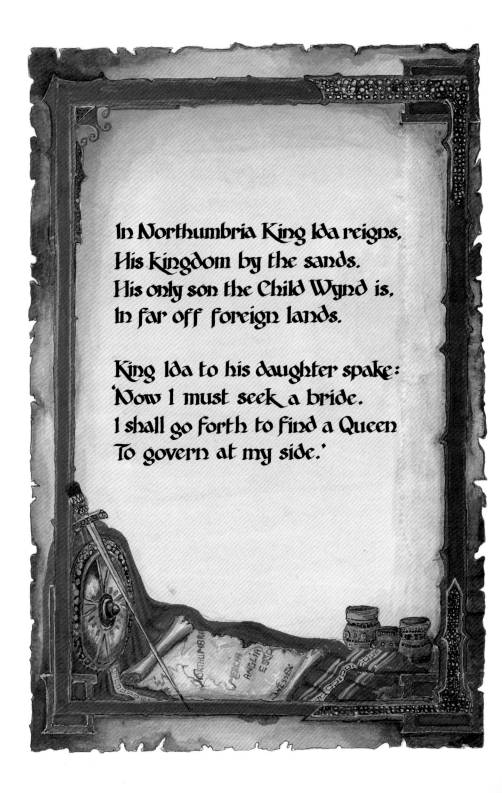

In Northumbria King Ida reigns,
His kingdom by the sands.
His only son the Child Wynd is,
In far off foreign lands.

King Ida to his daughter spake:
'Now I must seek a bride.
I shall go forth to find a Queen
To govern at my side.'

The King is gone from Bamborough Castle,
Long may the Princess mourn:
Long may she stand on the Castle wall,
Looking for his return.

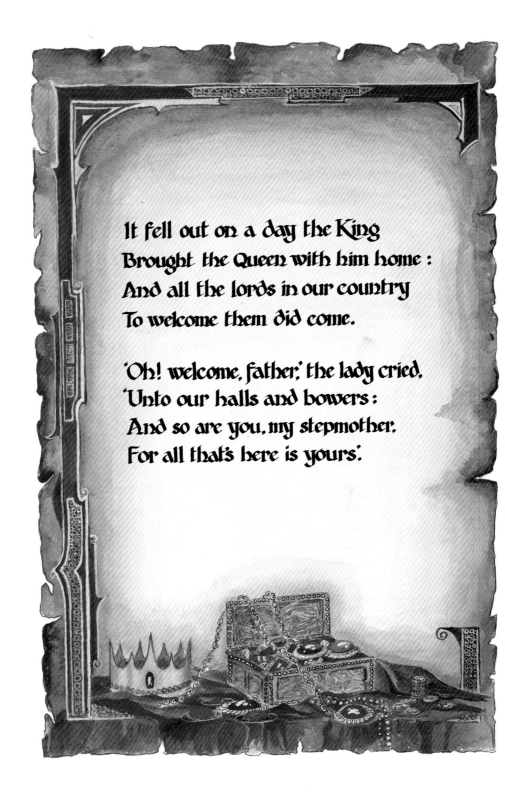

It fell out on a day the King
Brought the Queen with him home :
And all the lords in our country
To welcome them did come.

'Oh! welcome, father,' the lady cried,
'Unto our halls and bowers :
And so are you, my stepmother,
For all that's here is yours'.

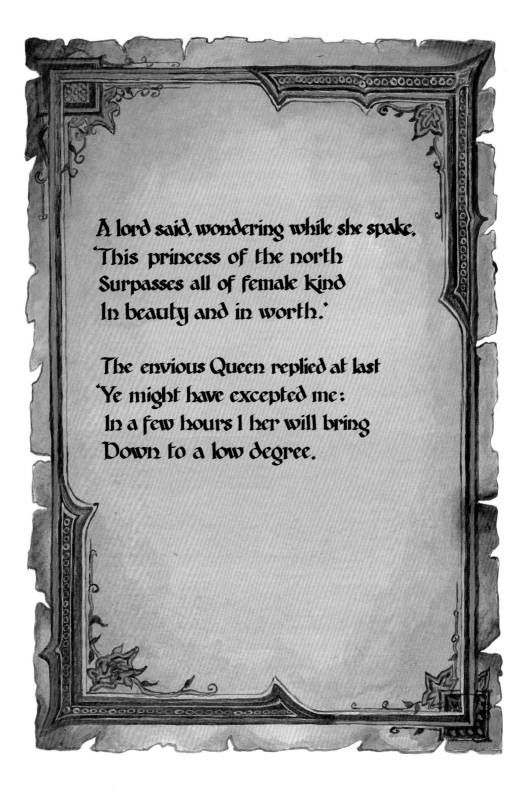

A lord said, wondering while she spake,
'This princess of the north
Surpasses all of female kind
In beauty and in worth.'

The envious Queen replied at last
'Ye might have excepted me:
In a few hours I her will bring
Down to a low degree.

'I will liken her to a Laidley worm,
That warps about the stone;
And not till Childy Wynd comes back
Shall she again be won.'

The Princess stood at her bower door
Laughing: who could her blame?
But e'er the next day's sun went down
A long worm she became.

Banished to live at Spindlestone Heugh,
Nigh a full league to the west,
She coiled about the Spindle Stone
And in a cave did rest.

For seven miles east and seven miles west,
And seven miles north and south,
No blade of grass or corn would grow,
So venemous was her mouth.

The milk of seven stately cows
(It was costly her to keep)
Was brought to her daily, which she drank
Before she went to sleep.

Word went east and word went west,
And over the sea did go;
The Child of Wynd got wit of it,
Which filled his heart with woe.

They built a ship without delay,
With masts of the rowan-tree
With flutt'ring sails of silk so fine,
And set her on the sea.

The Queen looked out of her bower window
To see what she could see;
There espied a gallant ship
Sailing upon the sea.

When she beheld the silken sails
Full glancing in the sun,
To sink the ship she sent away
Her witch wives every one.

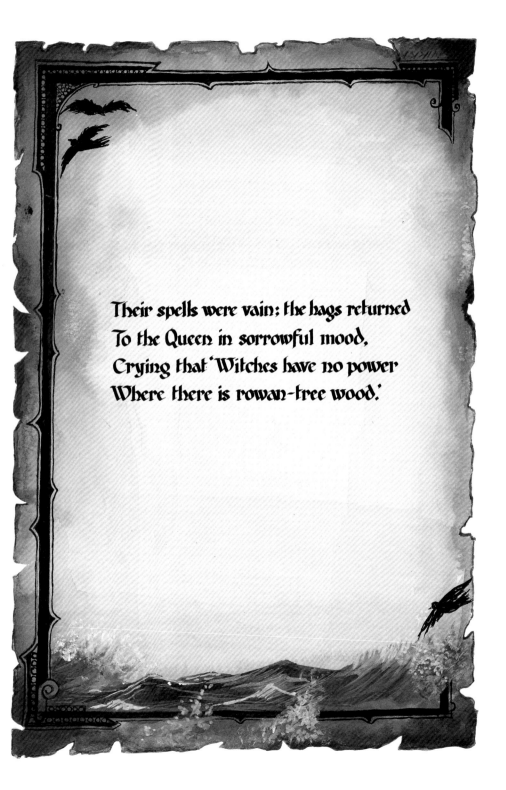

Their spells were vain; the hags returned
To the Queen in sorrowful mood,
Crying that 'Witches have no power
Where there is rowan-tree wood.'

The Child then ran out of her reach,
The ship on Budle sand;
And off he dashed to Spindlestone Heugh,
His weapon in his hand.

The Worm leapt up, the Worm leapt down,
She plaited round the stone.
Whenever the Child came near to her,
She thrust him off again.

And now he drew his berry-brown sword
And laid it on her head;
And swore if she did harm to him,
That he would strike her dead.

'Oh, quit thy sword and bend thy bow,
And give me kisses three;
If I'm not won e'er the sun go down,
Won I shall never be.'

He quitted his sword and bent his bow,
He gave her kisses three.
She shed the loathsome creature's skin
And of the curse was free.

Her absence and her serpent shape
The King had long deplored:
He now rejoiced to see them both
Again to him restored.

The Queen they wanted, whom they found
All pale and sore afraid,
Because she knew her power must yield
To Childy Wynd's, who said:

'I will turn you into a toad,
That on the ground doth wend,
And won, won shalt thou never be
Till this world hath an end.'

Now on the ground near Ida's tower
She crawls a loathsome toad,
And venom spits on every maid
She meets upon the road.

ISBN 0 902653 82 2

Published by Newcastle upon Tyne
City Libraries & Arts, 1991